The Watership Down

Film Picture Book

with linking text by
Richard Adams

Macmillan Publishing Co., Inc.
New York

Macmillan Publishing Co., Inc.
866 Third Avenue, New York, N.Y. 10022

Library of Congress Catalog Card Number: 78-24456
ISBN 0-02-016060-7
ISBN 0-02-500260-0 (cloth-bound edition)

First American Edition 1978

The Watership Down *Film Picture Book* is also published in a
reinforced cloth-bound edition by Macmillan Publishing Co., Inc.

Printed in the United States of America

Book design by David Pelham

Preface

A film is not a book. They are two distinct forms of art; and people who, when asked whether they have read a particular book, reply 'No, but I saw the film', might really just as sensibly answer, 'No, but I had breakfast this morning.' In a book, the author is talking to the reader and telling the story in his own individual way, in words. You have in your ears, as it were, the sound of his voice. When that story is re-told in the form of a film, drawing upon the book to a greater or lesser degree, the director of the film, not the author of the book, is telling the story in *his* own way; using, not prose, but moving pictures and dialogue. Because he is using different tools he does a different job. To that extent the two versions are bound to differ, even though they may retain much in common.

The film *Watership Down* is, I believe, a good one. However, it differs from the book in several places, partly because it would not be practicable to put everything into the film which is in the book – to try to do so would make the film far too long – and partly because telling the story, not in words but in pictures, action and dialogue, involves a different kind of flow and emphasis. To give two examples: first, in the book of *Watership Down*, the attack by the rats on Hazel and his friends during their journey to Watership Down is only briefly touched upon and happens, as it were, off-stage. The director of the film, however, realized that this attack would be exciting if the audience could actually *see* it, as opposed to just hearing about it, so he brought it 'on stage' and gave it much more emphasis than it gets in the book. Secondly, in the book the effect on the reader of the episode at Cowslip's warren is due principally to the mounting sense of mystery and misgiving in the minds of Hazel and his companions, and this is described in words. But as states of mind can't really be filmed, the director has shortened that episode, while sticking to the main point – what finally happened to Bigwig before the rabbits left.

This is a book of pictures from the film. It is emphatically *not* meant to be 'Watership Down told in pictures', or any kind of shortened, pictorial version of the novel. Indeed, in writing the captions for the pictures I have been at pains to avoid summarizing the story. People who want to read the story should read *Watership Down*; and people who want to know more about the pictures in this book should go and see the film.

One other thing I would like to say to anyone who looks at this book. If, having read *Watership Down*, you formed, in your own imagination, ideas of what Hazel, Fiver, Bigwig and the rest looked like, and those ideas are different from these pictures, then do please stick to your own ideas and forget the pictures. This book and the film represent the ideas of one group of people, but yours are as good as theirs, whether you are six or eighty-six or any age between. If it comes to that, I don't, myself, much like their Fiver – he is not how I imagine him. Never mind. You might not like *my* Fiver – especially as I can't draw. On the other hand, I personally happen to like their Hazel very much; and their Hyzenthlay. And I admire the film as a whole. It's all simply a matter of how it strikes your own imagination.

I hope this book will give people pleasure and that it may make them want to do each of two different things – see the film; and read the book.

Richard Adams

Foreword

I first read *Watership Down* while in India on a location survey for another film, and was immediately captivated by it. To my surprise, Hazel, Fiver, Bigwig and company quickly became much more than simply a band of rabbits created out of Richard Adams's mind: I cared about them and their adventure and wanted to share with others the excitement of my discovery. The difficulty involved in transforming the intricate patterns of rabbit life to the screen would become evident later, but during those heady days following my first reading I was convinced that a unique motion picture could emerge from the story.

One of the first problems we had to overcome was the look of the animals themselves. One rabbit looks much like another to the untrained eye, and as we would be dealing with a large group of rabbit 'actors', the problem was considerably magnified. The final designs of the principal characters in the film depend largely upon size, both skeletal and muscular, with colour and visual markings – Bigwig's top-knot and the dark patch on Blackberry's head are examples – playing an important role.

Much of the appeal of the book lies in Richard Adams's marvellously evocative and accurate picture of the English countryside, and it was essential that the film retain that quality. Again a problem arose: if the rabbits were too realistically drawn, they tended to disappear into the background, as they do in nature; if too broadly drawn, they clashed with the naturalistic backgrounds. In the end a fine line was established between the two, and the actual locations described in the book – Nuthanger Farm, the Enbourne, the River Test – were painted each at the correct season by a team of enthusiastic and talented artists.

Subtlety, whether in character or story-telling, is a quality rarely seen in animated films, and there are valid reasons for this. In a live action film, it is possible to cut out one frame and that single picture will, in a sense, tell a story. Complex movements of the human face caught by the camera can, for example, convey subtle emotions and thoughts. But any single frame of an animated film depends for its effect on the frames that precede and follow it – it is the animation itself that gives life to the story.

Because of this, animated films have tended to overstate, going 'over the top' into broad comedy, violence or 'magical' transformations to create scenes impossible to reproduce in a live action film.

The film of *Watership Down* is something altogether different. The story works on many levels, which depend not only on 'effects' but on character development and carefully calculated revelation. Consequently, certain demands are made on the audience which they have not been used to in animation before. I hope a new and enjoyable film experience will be the reward.

Martin Rosen

Director/Producer/Writer of the film Watership Down.

Long ago Frith made the world.

Frith made all the animals and birds, but when he first made them they were all the same

El-ahrairah was among the animals in those days... and after a time the rabbits wandered everywhere, multiplying and eating as they went.

Then Frith said to El-ahrairah, 'Prince Rabbit, if you cannot control your people, I shall find ways to control them. So mark what I say.' But El-ahrairah would not listen and he said to Frith, 'My people are the strongest in the world, for they breed faster and eat more than any of the other people.'

Frith determined to get the better of El-ahrairah not by means of his own great power but by means of a trick. He gave out that he would hold a great meeting and that at that meeting he would give a present to every animal and bird, to make each one different from the rest . . . And so in their turn came the fox and the stoat and the weasel.

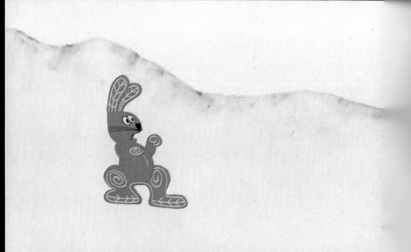

Then Frith felt himself in friendship with El-ahrairah, and he said, 'Very well. Bottom, be strength and warning and speed for ever.'
El-ahrairah's tail grew shining white and flashed like a star; and his back legs grew long and powerful and he tore across the hill faster than any creature in the world . . .

And Frith called after him, 'All the world will be your enemy, Prince with a Thousand Enemies, and whenever they catch you they will kill you. But first they must catch you, digger, listener, runner, prince with the swift warning. Be cunning and full of tricks and your people shall never be destroyed.'

Hazel comes out of his hole, followed by Fiver, for the evening silflay.

Fiver finds a cowslip,

but he and Hazel are

driven off it by Toadflax and another member of the Owsla.

as blood covering the whole field.

Fiver, in the shadow of the new and inexplicable notice-board,

tries to explain to Hazel his sense of dread.

Hazel telling Bigwig that he and Fiver want to see the Chief Rabbit.

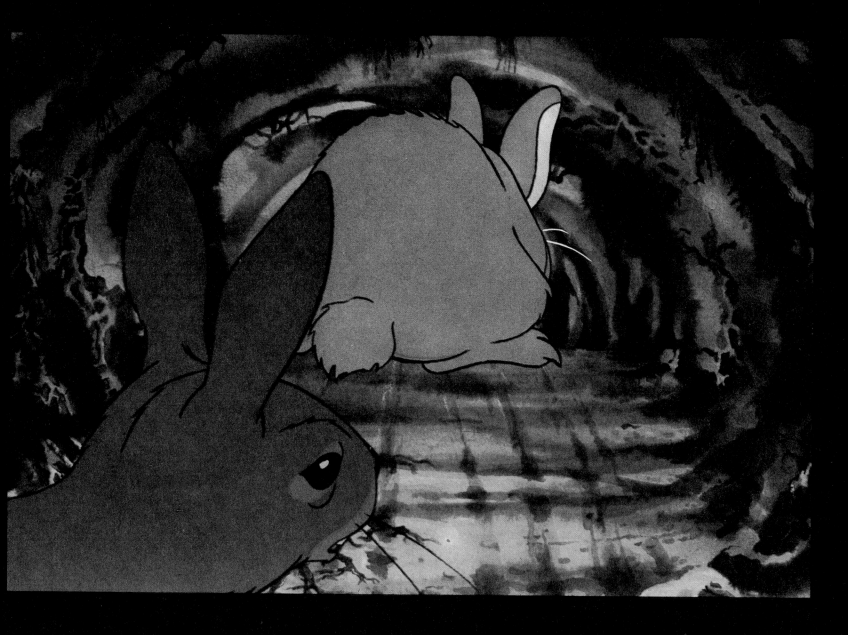

Blackberry and others listening outside the Chief Rabbit's burrow.

Bigwig asks Hazel and his small band

of rabbits about their intention to leave the warren.

Hazel and his rabbits

HAZEL: That was a good idea of yours, Blackberry.
BLACKBERRY: Yes, let's try to remember it. It might

The fields beyond the Enborne.

The rabbits shelter and rest in the cover of the bean field.

They come to Newtown

churchyard at night.

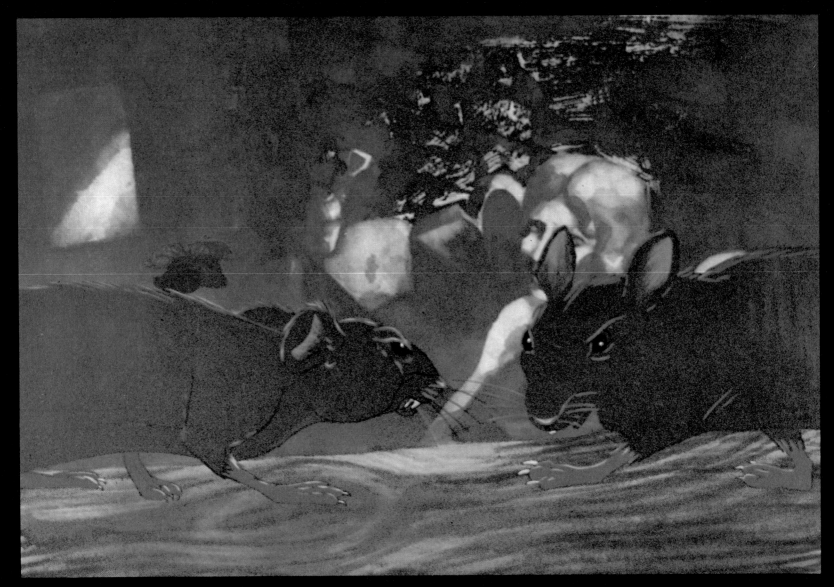

The rabbits, sheltering in an outbuilding

take to flight once again.

The following day, while trying to shelter from heavy rain,
their thoughts turn to the warren they left two nights ago.

They feel themselves in continual danger. Where are they supposed to be going, and has Hazel got any real plan?

Fiver is convinced that they must go on until they reach the distant hills. Bigwig becomes angry with some of the other rabbits, who disagree. They seem about to quarrel when

suddenly, an unknown rabbit, a stranger, appears.
In reply to questions, he tells them that his name is Cowslip.

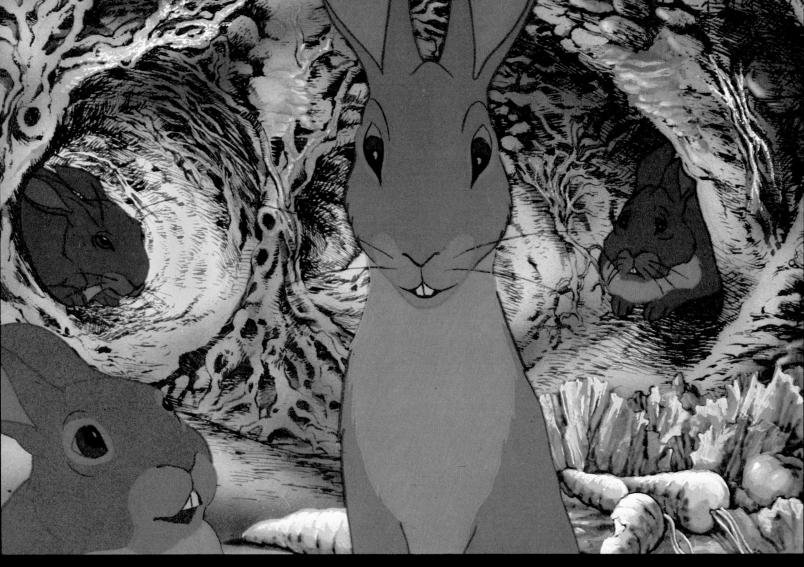

They find friendly, well-fed rabbits and a plentiful supply of carrots.

The rabbits puzzled by the curious smell, the plentiful food
and the strange manner of the rabbits in Cowslip's warren.

Pipkin, watched by Cowslip, feels misgivings. To him
the strange rabbits seem 'sad, like trees in November'.

Hazel follows Fiver out of Cowslip's warren and across the field.

as Bigwig struggles and chokes in the wire.

Fiver bites through the peg.

The rabbits gather round Bigwig, wondering whether he is already dead.

Unexpectedly, when they have given him up, Bigwig revives.

Fiver explaining the terrible secret of Cowslip's warren
and advising immediate departure.

The rabbits, looking out across the fields,

get their first sight of the distant Downs.

Nuthanger Farm, which Hazel, taking Pipkin with him,
first visits on the way to Watership Down.*

in the outhouse, and talks to Clover about the idea of escape.

Hazel warned by Pipkin

that a cat is coming.

As the voice inexplicably calls him by name, Bigwig,
believing it to be the Black Rabbit of Inlé, feels compelled
to go out to meet him.

Captain Holly falling in among the rabbits.

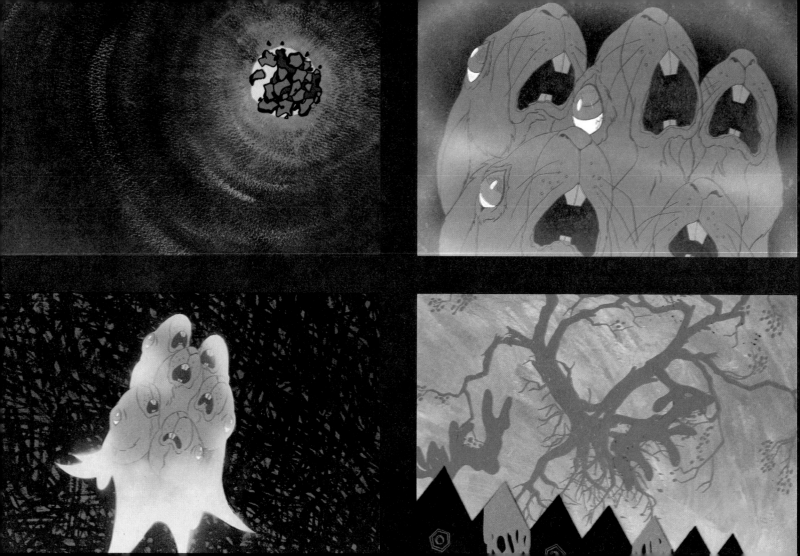

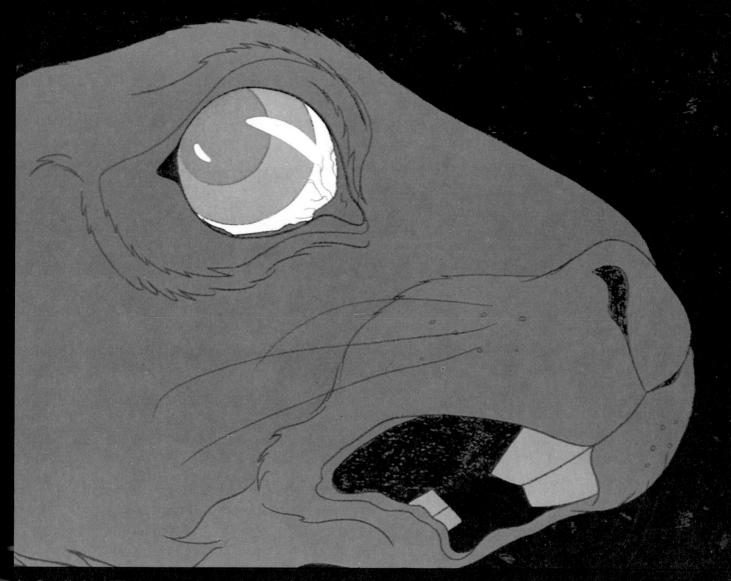
the Sandleford Warren by poison-gas and bulldozer.

Holly speaks of being wounded, during his journey, in a

place called Efrafa, but collapses, exhausted, before he can say more.

Watership Down.

HAZEL: Let me get this straight, Fiver.
You want us to climb this, is that it?

Hazel going up Watership Down for the first time,

followed by the other rabbits.

DANDELION: You can see the whole world!
O Frith on the hills! He made it all for us!

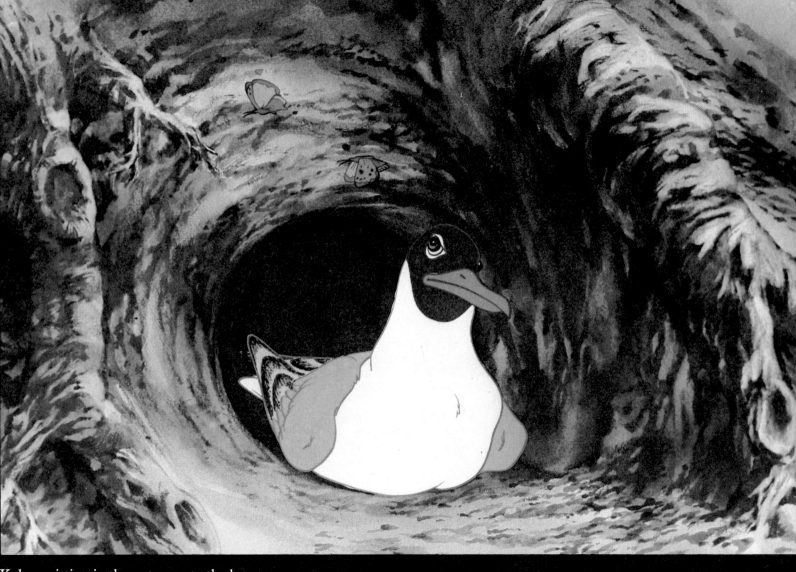

Kehaar sitting in the entrance to the burrow.

Hazel, Bigwig and Blackberry basking in the sun at evening silflay.

Hazel points out to Blackberry that their new warren has no
does, without which it cannot survive. He puts forward the
idea of a raid on Nuthanger Farm to free some of the hutch
does to join them in the wild.

Bigwig, finding Kehaar at the entrance to the burrow,

FIVER: It's no good asking you not to go, I suppose?
HAZEL: It will be perfectly safe, Fiver. I'll take the greatest care.

Clover, asleep among the other hutch rabbits, is startled by the sound
of Hazel and Dandelion approaching to break open the hutch.

Hazel and Dandelion on top of the hutch.

Their enemies

give the alarm –

and the danger grows –

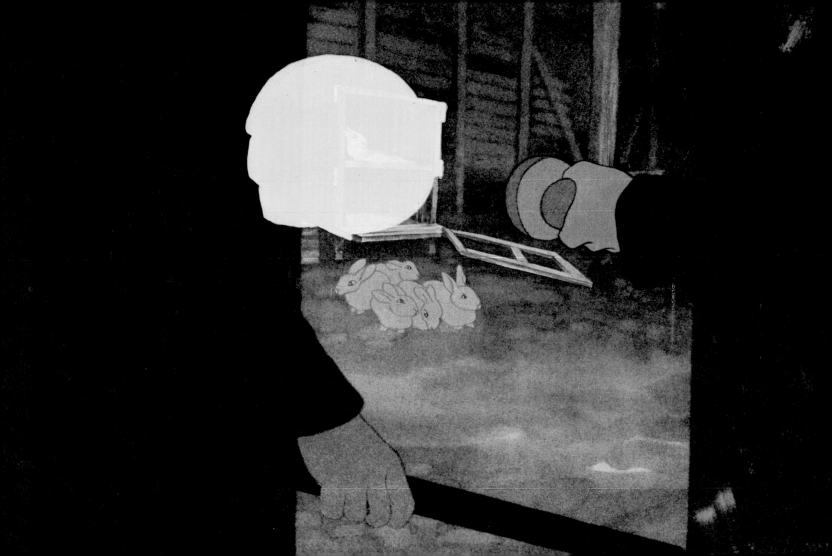

The farmer shoots at Hazel.

Fiver, anxiously awaiting Hazel's return.

s told by Dandelion and Blackberry that Hazel has been shot

Fiver, led by a mysterious vision,

reaches the mouth of the drain in which Hazel is lying wounded by the gun.

Kehaar

returns from his reconnaissance flight.

Kehaar picking the shot-gun pellets out of Hazel's wound.

The rabbits, at silflay on the Down, are told by Kehaar
that he has seen Efrafa. Holly now tells them –

of how they wounded him during his journey to the Down,

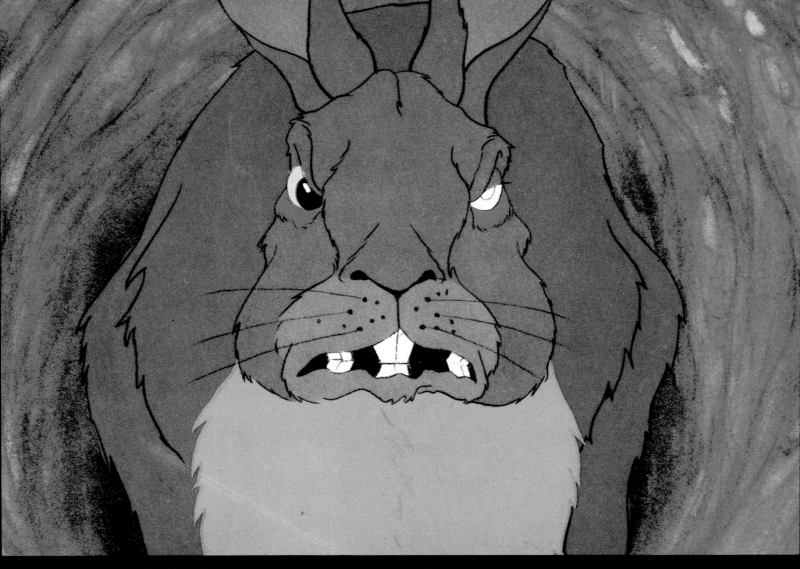

of their terrible leader, General Woundwort,

of the Mark Captains who carry out his orders,

Efrafa is overcrowded, but Woundwort, despite Hyzenthlay's representations, will allow no rabbits to leave.

Holly tells how

They continue their journey towards Efrafa.

The rabbits come to the railway arch,

meets Captain Campion and Captain Vervain,

who bring him before

General Woundwort.

Bigwig, guarded by Captain Campion, tells General
Woundwort that he has come to join Efrafa.

Captain Campion inflicts upon Bigwig one of the customary

Hazel and his band arrive on the banks of the river Test and find the punt.

HAZEL: What on earth's that, Kehaar?
KEHAAR: (gulps): Heem feesh!

Bigwig takes up his duties as an officer of the Near Hind Mark.

Bigwig comes upon Hyzenthlay and some of the other does
during the Near Hind Mark silflay.

BIGWIG: Will you join us – and persuade your friends as well?
HYZENTHLAY: My courage – my spirit. It's so much less than it was.

Bigwig telling Kehaar to be ready for his break-out from
Efrafa at sunset that evening.

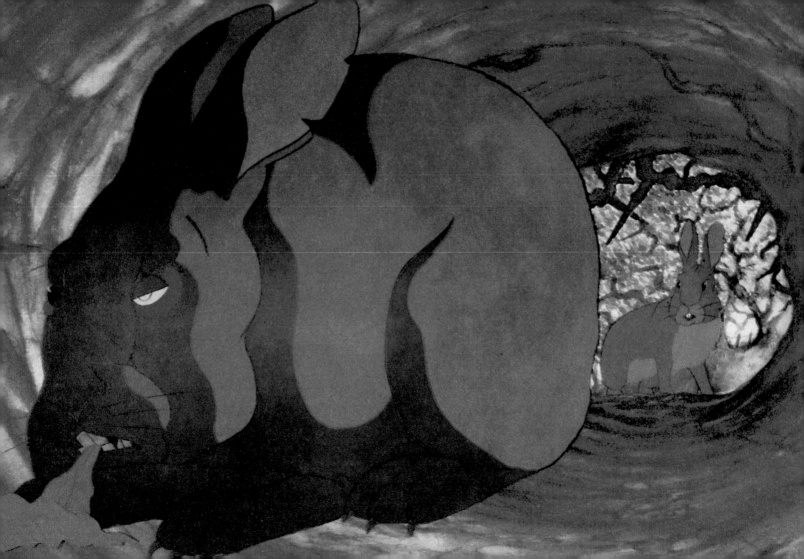

Bigwig, on the run with Blackavar and the does, glances
back to see whether they are being pursued.

The pursuit, led by General Woundwort, sets out from Efrafa.

Kehaar watching Bigwig's escape from the top of the railway arch.

HYZENTHLAY: Bigwig, where's the bird?
BIGWIG: He'll be here. He'd better be.

As the thunderstorm begins, Hazel, Fiver and Silver anxiously
await Bigwig on the river-bank.

Kehaar about to dive from the bridge in the storm.

WOUNDWORT: I'll settle with you myself, Bigwig.
There's no need to take *you* back.
BIGWIG: You crack-brained slave-driver, I'd like to see you try.

Kehaar dives into action

to save Bigwig as Woundwort is about to attack him.

Bigwig lashes out at Woundwort,

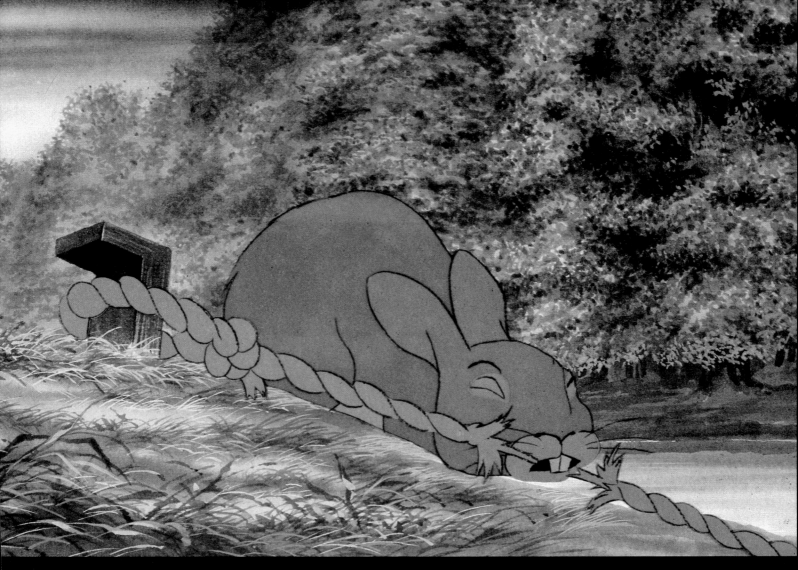

Hazel severs the rope,

and leaps

KEHAAR: You go. I go. Ees finished 'ere for me. I go to peeg vater!

The rabbits are at silflay on Watership Down,

when Silver brings the appalling news that General
Woundwort is approaching with a strong force of Efrafans.

HAZEL: Fill in the holes!

Hazel, with Campion and Vervain on either side of him,
trying to come to terms with General Woundwort

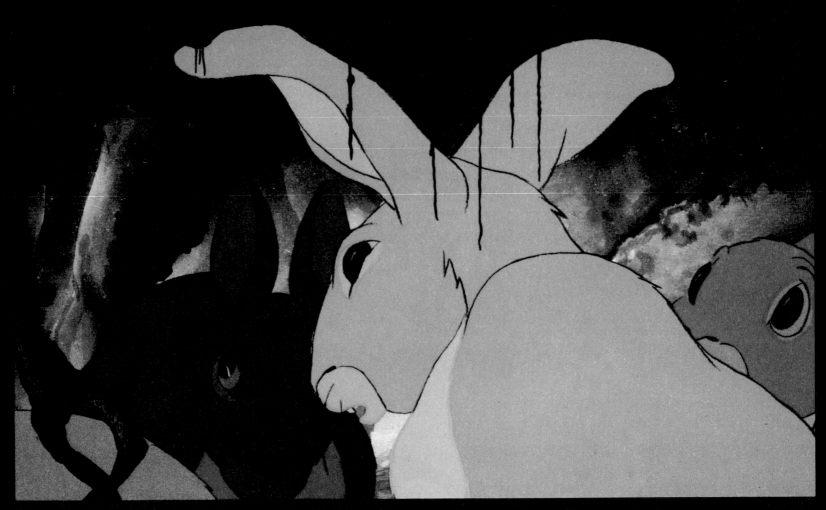

Hazel, whose life Woundwort has scornfully spared in order
that he may take back the Efrafan terms, returns to the burrow.

The Efrafans begin digging their way in.

FIVER: I – I'm trying to listen . . . Only I can't hear it. I'm going away, Hazel.

'It's cold! How – how cold! … There's a dog loose in the wood!'

HAZEL: Bigwig, I need runners!

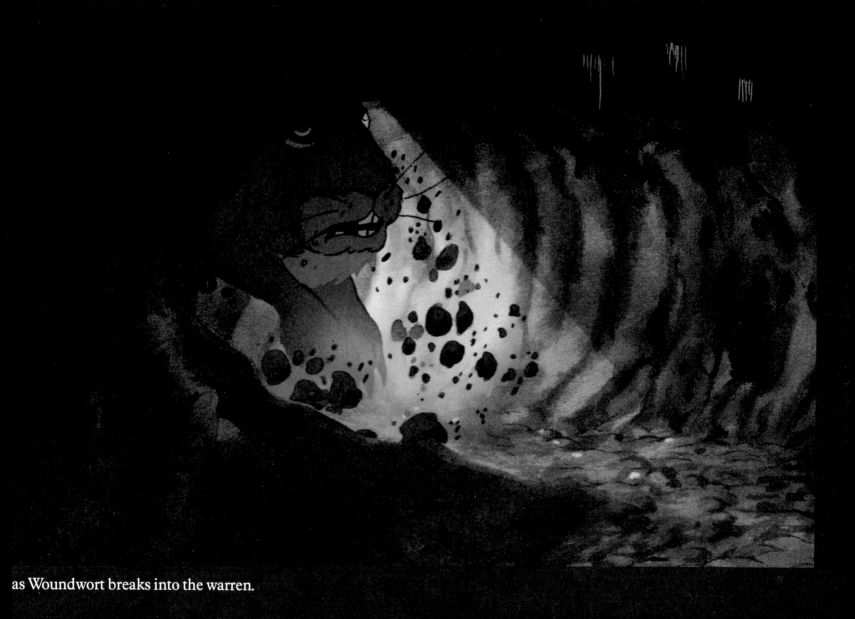

as Woundwort breaks into the warren.

Woundwort makes his way deeper into the warren.

Pipkin covering Bigwig with earth, so that he can lie concealed and make a surprise attack on General Woundwort.

Hazel and Dandelion, having left Blackberry in hiding
behind a tree-stump on the verge of the road, arrive at

The dog is asleep at the mouth of its kennel.

Hazel, on the roof of the kennel, sets about gnawing the dog's rope.

The dog, having spotted Dandelion, about to leap out of its kennel.

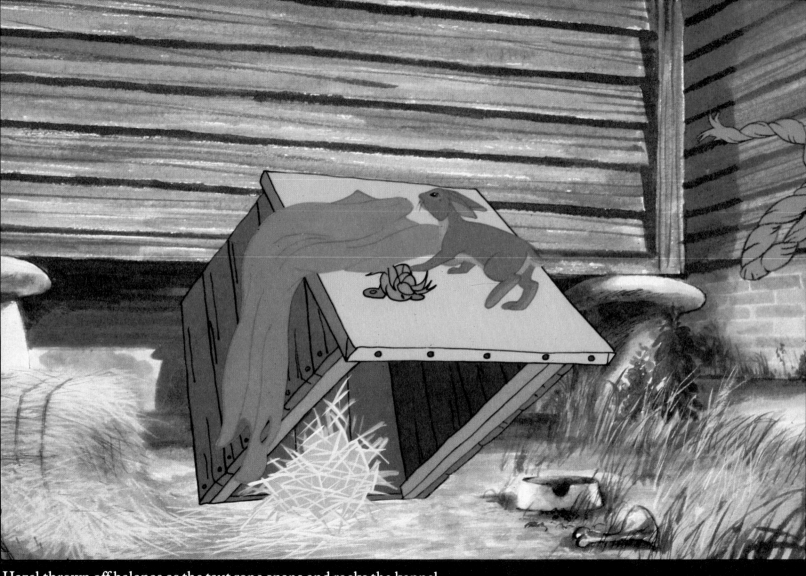

Hazel thrown off balance as the taut rope snaps and rocks the kennel.

THE CAT: Can you run? I think not. I think not.

LUCY: Tab! Tab! Let'n alone!

Woundwort encounters Pipkin.

Pipkin and some of the other rabbits backing away as Woundwort advances.

Dandelion drawing the

Bigwig and General Woundwort.

Blackberry takes over from

Dandelion and draws the dog on into the field below the Down.

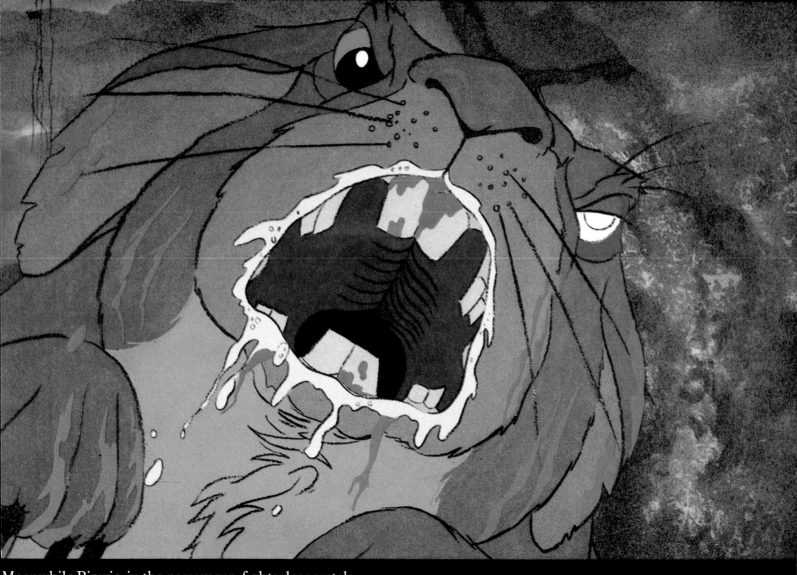

Meanwhile Bigwig, in the narrow run, fights desperately
to prevent General Woundwort from breaking in among the other
rabbits further back.

IGWIG: I told you once I was trying to impress you. I hope I have.
OUNDWORT: I told you I would kill you myself. There is no white bird here, Bigwig.

The dog reaches the iron tree

...and Hyzenthlay takes over the task of luring it up the Down.

BIGWIG: My Chief Rabbit has told me to defend this run.
WOUNDWORT (amazed): Your Chief Rabbit?

The dog plunging in among the Efrafans outside the warren.

CAPTAIN CAMPION: Run! Run for your lives!

killing and scattering the Efrafans.

dangerous! Come back and fight!

Such was Woundwort's monument:
and perhaps it would not have displeased him.

"You needn't worry about them," said his companion.
"They'll be all right, and thousands like them. If you'll
come along, I'll show you what I mean."

He reached the top of the bank in a single, powerful leap.
Hazel followed; and together they slipped away. . .'

Long ago, Frith made the world.

THE LAPINE GLOSSARY

(Courtesy of Richard Adams, Author of Watership Down*)*

According to Richard Adams, the best (in fact the only) living authority on the subject, rabbits speak English but have their own language, as well.

For instance, rabbits can count only up to four. Anything over that number, from five to a million, is called "U Hrair," which translates roughly as "a lot."

For a quick course in lapine language, and to help you enjoy the fun and adventure of *Watership Down*, the following is an abridged rabbit dictionary...

Efrafa
The name of the warren founded by General Woundwort.

El-ahrairah
The rabbit folk hero. The name means the Prince with a Thousand Enemies.

Flayrah
Unusually good food, e.g., lettuce.

Frith
The sun, personified as a god by rabbits.

Hraka
Droppings.

Hrududu
A tractor, car or any motor vehicle.

Inlé
Literally, the moon; also moonrise. But a second meaning carries the idea of darkness, fear and death.

Lendri
A badger.

Ni-Frith
Noon.

Owsla
The strongest rabbits in a warren, the ruling clique.

Rah
A prince, leader or chief rabbit.

Silflay
To go above ground to feed.

MARTIN ROSEN'S PRODUCTION OF

Watership Down

Music composed by.. Angela Morley
'Bright Eyes' composed by.. Mike Batt
and sung by... Art Garfunkel
Music Director... Marcus Dods
Animation Supervisor... Philip Duncan
Director of Animation...Tony Guy

Written for the Screen, Produced and Directed by
MARTIN ROSEN

NEPENTHE PRODUCTIONS LIMITED
Soundtrack Released by CBS Records and Tapes